Presented to Ruth an[d]
by Mr & Mrs. Merb Newell
(Merb & Georgia)
for perfect attendance for 6 month
(Jan to June 1964)

YO-ATH-575

BASIC BIBLE READER: GRADE TWO

I read about
God's Gifts

by Carol Ferntheil

Illustrated by

Vera Gohman

STANDARD PUBLISHING
CINCINNATI, OHIO   2712

FOLLOWING A TRADITION

The new Basic Bible Readers are a beautiful, up-to-date edition of the famous Standard Bible Story Readers, by Lillie A. Faris, that were first printed in 1925. More than a million copies of the earlier editions have been added to the libraries of homes, schools, and churches in the past four decades.

The best of the former readers has been retained in this new series, including the favorite Bible stories that forever appeal to our children. However, all of the illustrations are completely new—drawn by noted children's artists of today.

© MCMLXII, THE STANDARD PUBLISHING COMPANY

Cincinnati, Ohio   Printed in U.S.A.

Introduction

In the public schools today, the child has practically no contact with the Bible. The home and the Bible school must provide the opportunities and the materials if the child is to learn to read the Bible with pleasure and understanding.

The *second-grade child* reading this book will add to his vocabulary words that he must know in order to read the Bible. The word lists beginning on page 124 make it possible for him to refer to Bible words as he uses the book, just as he learns new words from his public school reader. If he is not at all familiar with Bible words, it would be wise to give him first the Basic Bible Reader, Grade One: *I Read About God's Love.*

The *parents* may plan family devotions around some of the stories or poems in this book, so that the child can contribute by reading aloud. Stories that are read sometimes from the Bible, may at other times be read from this book. Children may be encouraged to follow up Bible-school lessons by reading the stories in their own Basic Bible Readers.

The *Bible-school teacher* will find this book particularly useful in any unit emphasizing God's gifts to us, as well as in other studies on the life of Christ or in teaching various Old Testament stories. It will be a valuable addition to the reading table.

If a book is provided for each class member, then class time may be used for group reading of stories. When drill is needed for recognizing and understanding certain Bible words, the teacher can choose sentences and pages where that word is used.

The *librarian* will find this a useful book for parents and teachers to borrow as they plan how to tell Bible stories to second-graders or as they try to decide what religious books to buy for children. Its library use should not be limited to adults. Children who do not own it should be allowed to borrow it from the library to read at home.

If the librarian presents a story hour, these stories provide some good selections for use. The poems may be recommended when there are requests for selections to memorize.

DEDICATION

This book is lovingly dedicated to those boys and girls who are beginning to read for themselves the wonderful story of God's love.

Stories

God Sends His Son............... *Matthew 2:1-12* 8

One Starry Night................ *Luke 2:8-20* 15

Jesus Grows Up................. *Luke 2:39, 40* 18

Jesus Calls His Helpers........ *Matthew 4:18-22; Luke 5:27, 28*.. 20

A Hole in the Roof............. *Luke 5:18-26* 24

By a Wonderful Pool........... *John 5:2-9* 30

A Hand to Work for Jesus...... *Luke 6:6-10* 35

Jesus Makes People Well....... *Matthew 8:1-13; Luke 7:1-10*.... 41

A Big Storm.................... *Mark 4:36-41* 44

A Little Lunch Basket.......... *John 6:1-14* 50

Jesus and a Blind Man.......... *John 9:1, 6-12* 57

A Man on a Trip............... *Luke 10:30-37* 61

A Man Says Thank You......... *Luke 17:12-19* 66

Jesus and the Children........ *Mark 10:13-16* 71

A Man in a Tree............... *Luke 19:1-10* 74

Jesus' Good Friends........... *Luke 10:38-42; John 11:1-44;*
12:1-8 78

Jesus Says Good-by............ *John 14* 81

Jesus Goes Home.............. *John 19:16-19; Luke 24*....... 84

The New Coat.................. 90

God Made the World........... *Genesis 1—2:8, 20-23; 3:20*..... 96

The Great Ladder............. *Genesis 28:10-22* 100

God Sends Food............... *Exodus 15:22-25; 17:1-6;*
16:11-13 104

The Fall of Jericho............ *Joshua 6:1-16, 20* 108

David Helps the King.......... *1 Samuel 16:11-23; 17:13-15*.... 112

David and the Giant............ *1 Samuel 17:17-51* 115

Bread for Elijah................ *1 Kings 17* 120

Bible Verses

The Lord's Prayer...........*Matthew 6:10-13* 38
"Let Not Your Heart Be
    Troubled" ....*John 14:1-3* 82

Poems

Blessed Christmas... 12
What Can I Give Him?...................................... 14
The Golden Rule... 40
Praise God.. 87
Father, We Thank Thee..................................... 88

Also in This Book

Introduction 3
New Basic Bible Vocabulary................................ 124
Cumulative Basic Bible Vocabulary......................... 126

God
Sends
His
Son

Some very wise men lived in a land far
away from Bethlehem.

They did not know Mary.

They did not know Joseph.

But they knew that a new King was
born in Bethlehem.

They wanted to worship Him.

The Wise-men traveled miles and miles to see the baby Jesus.

They brought Him wonderful presents.

They worshiped Him.

They knew that He was to be a great king of His people.

He would be worshiped and loved.

The Wise-men had read God's words.

They knew that the star would show them where the new King was.

One night they saw the bright star.

It was brighter than all the others.

The Wise-men got ready for a trip.

They found gifts to take to the King.

They climbed on their camels.

They did not know the way. But God showed them where to go.

The bright star moved in the sky.

The star took them to Jerusalem. They went to King Herod's house.

"Where is the new King?" they asked.

King Herod asked many men.

They said the new King of the Jews was to be born in Bethlehem.

"Go to Bethlehem," Herod told the Wise-men. "If you find Him, come back and tell me about Him."

The Wise-men went to Bethlehem. They found baby Jesus, the new King. They gave Him their gifts. They worshiped Him.

The baby Jesus was God's own Son. God knew that King Herod might hurt Him.

God told the Wise-men not to go back to see King Herod.

The Wise-men went home another way.

They loved the baby Jesus. They were happy to give Him nice gifts.

Blessed Christmas

The sweetest day of all the year,
Is blessed, blessed Christmas;
To all the little children dear,
'Tis blessed, blessed Christmas.

'Twas then the Christ child came
    to earth,
At blessed, blessed Christmas;
And still we hail His holy birth,
At blessed, blessed Christmas.

And so we deck our homes today,
For blessed, blessed Christmas;
We'll love and honor Him alway;
For blessed, blessed Christmas.

What Can I Give Him?

What can I give Him,
Poor as I am?
If I were a shepherd,
I would bring a lamb.

If I were a Wise-man,
I would do my part.
Yet what can I give Him?
Give Him my heart.

—*Christina G. Rossetti*

One Starry Night

It was a beautiful night. There were many stars in the sky.

The shepherds were in the field. They had to watch their sheep all night.

Then there was a bright light. It was brighter than the light from the stars. The shepherds were afraid.

They saw an angel in the light. "Do not be afraid," the angel said. "I bring you good news. It is happy news for all people.

"A Saviour was born today. He is Christ the Lord. He was born in the city of Bethlehem."

The shepherds wanted to see the baby.
The angel told them this:

"You can find the baby. He is sleeping
in a manger. He is dressed in warm baby
clothes."

Then the light got brighter. There were many angels in the sky. The angels were singing this song:

> Glory to God in the highest,
> and on earth peace,
> good will toward men.

Then the bright light was gone.
The angels were gone.
The shepherds said, "God has sent us this news. Let us go see this baby who is Christ the Lord."
The shepherds walked across the fields to Bethlehem.
They found the stable where Mary and Joseph were. They saw the manger. And there they saw the baby Jesus.
The shepherds worshiped the baby. They knew He was Christ the Lord. The angels had told them the news on this beautiful starry night.

JESUS GROWS UP

Jesus lived in a house in the city of Nazareth.

His mother, Mary, was very busy. She had to cook the food and sew the clothes. She had to carry water from the well and shop at the market.

Sometimes Jesus helped her. He liked to help His mother. She took good care of Him.

Sometimes Jesus helped Joseph in his carpenter work. He liked to look at Joseph's things. He was happy when Joseph said, "You may use this hammer and saw."

Then Jesus used the hammer. He used the saw. He liked to help Joseph.

Sometimes Jesus played with other children. They played games like the ones you play.

Sometimes they had running races. They had a good time.

Jesus grew and grew. He learned many things. Mary told Him the stories about God's people. She told Him about God, His Father in heaven. Jesus was a happy boy. He was growing up.

Jesus Calls His Helpers

Jesus grew to be a man. He had work to do.

He had to tell people about God, His Father in heaven. He had to tell people how to be good.

He wanted to make people well so they would know He was the Son of God.

Jesus needed helpers. He needed men to help Him teach people. He needed men to help Him on His long trips.

Jesus looked for men who would be good helpers. He needed hard workers.

Jesus went into a big city. He looked at all the people.

Jesus was careful. He needed good helpers.

Then He saw Matthew. Matthew was sitting at a table. He had money on it.

People gave him money for the king. Matthew was very rich.

Jesus needed Matthew for a helper. People said, "Matthew is rich. He can not live as a rich man if he goes with Jesus. He will not want to leave his money."

But Jesus called, "Follow me."

Matthew looked at Jesus. He looked at his money. What would he do?

Matthew left the money. He loved Jesus. He wanted to be a helper.

People were surprised. But Matthew was a good helper for Jesus.

One day Jesus walked by the sea. He saw two brothers. They were fishing. Their names were Peter and Andrew.

Jesus said to Peter and Andrew, "Follow me, and I will make you fishers of men."

Peter and Andrew left their fishing boats. They left their fishing nets. They loved Jesus. They were happy to be His helpers. They were happy to go with Jesus.

Jesus saw two more brothers. Their names were James and John. They were working on their fishing nets.

Jesus called, "Follow me."

James and John left their fishing nets. They loved Jesus. They wanted to be His helpers, too.

A Hole in the Roof

A man was very sick. His hands would not be still.

And his legs would not be still. If he tried to stand, he would fall over.

No one could make him well.

One day his friends heard some good news. "Jesus is here again," they said.

"We must try to take you to Jesus. He can make you well."

"But I can not go and see Jesus," the sick man said. "I can not walk."

His friends had a good idea.

"We will take you to Jesus," they said. "You can lie on your bed."

The sick man's bed was not very big or heavy. His friends walked slowly down the street.

It was easy to see where Jesus was. There were many people around the house. There was a crowd of people around the door. So many people had tried to get inside to hear Jesus.

Where would they take the sick man on his bed? They could not get inside through the door of the house.

They thought of the little stairway on the outside of the house.

They said, "Let us carry him up the stairway. Then we will be on the roof. Jesus will be in the room under us.

"Then we can take out some pieces of the roof. That will make a hole in the roof.

"We will put the bed down through the hole. Jesus will see that our sick friend needs help."

This is just what they did.

They walked up the stairway. They put the bed down on the flat roof. They tied long ropes around the bed.

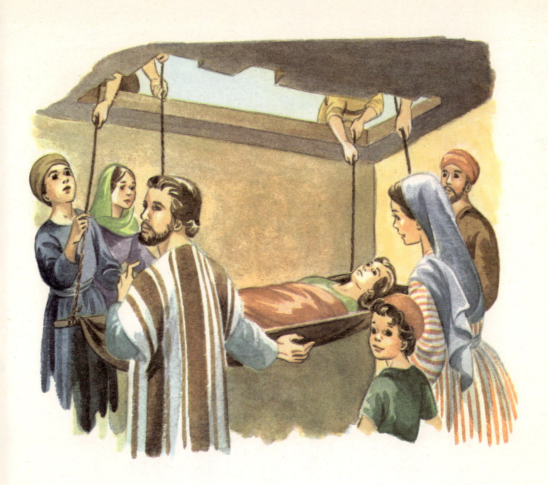

They took out some of the pieces of the roof. They made a big hole.

They picked up the bed. They were very careful not to hurt their friend.

They held on to the ropes. Down, down, down through the hole in the roof went the bed with their sick friend.

The bed went down through the hole right to the place where Jesus was standing in the house.

Jesus saw the sick man who could not walk or feed himself.

Jesus was happy that the man wanted to come to see Him.

Jesus was pleased because the man's friends said that He could make the sick man well.

Jesus wanted every one to know that He could make people well.

He said to the sick man, "Stand up, take up your bed, and walk."

Then a wonderful thing happened!

The sick man got up. He was able to stand up. He was able to walk.

Every one saw him stand and walk. Every one knew that Jesus had made him well.

The man picked up his bed. He took it home. He walked all the way.

He told every one what Jesus had done. He said thank you to Jesus all the time for making him well.

His friends were happy, too. They put the pieces back on the roof. They walked home, too. They told every one that Jesus had made their friend well.

By a Wonderful Pool

Many sick people were walking through the streets. Some were helped by their friends. Some were carried. There were all kinds of sick people.

"Where are all the sick people going?" some one said.

"To the pool of Bethesda," they said.

"We hope to get well there," some of the sick people answered.

"It is a wonderful place. Sometimes an angel comes to stir up the water in the pool.

"When the angel leaves, the sick people get into the pool.

"The first one to get into the pool is made well again."

One sick man always went to the pool of Bethesda.

He had not been able to walk for 38 years.

The sick man knew when the angel would come. He knew that the angel would stir up the water.

He knew that the first one to get into the water would be made well. If only he could be that first one!

He had his bed near the pool. But he could not get up from his bed. He needed some one to help him.

He would pray that some one would help him.

The sick man prayed for help.

Then some one did come to help him. It was Jesus.

Jesus walked by the wonderful pool of Bethesda.

"Would you like to be made well?" Jesus asked the man.

The sick man said, "Oh, yes, I would like to be well, but there is no one to help me get into the water.

"When the angel comes to the water, I must be the first one to get into the pool. But there is no one to help me. I can never be the first one."

Jesus was sorry. He wanted to help the sick man. But He did not have to wait for the angel to come.

Jesus was the Son of God. He could make people well any time.

Jesus said to the man, "Stand up, take up your bed, and walk."

The man was well. He could stand up. He did not need help.

All the people saw the man get up. They saw that Jesus made him well.

The man was very happy. He could pick up his bed. He could walk home.

He did not have to wait by the pool any longer. Jesus had come. Jesus had made him well.

A Hand to Work for Jesus

Here is something to try: Hold one hand behind your back. Suppose you could not use that hand. What do you think you would do?

It would be hard to help your mother. It would be hard to do your work in school. It would be hard to play. It would be hard to work for Jesus.

One day Jesus saw a man who could not use his hand.

Jesus saw the man in God's house. It was the day when every one went to God's house to worship and pray.

Jesus and His friends always went to God's house.

The man who could not use his hand was in God's house, too.

Jesus saw that the hand was very small. It was not like your hand. This man's hand would not hold things. It would not pick up things.

The man tried and tried to use his hand. But he could not use it.

Jesus felt sorry for the man. He knew how sad the man must be.

Jesus was always glad to help people. He wanted to help the man who could not use his hand.

Jesus said to the man, "Stand up."

The man stood up. Then Jesus said, "Hold out your hand."

The man held out his hand. His hand was well. He could use it.

Now the man could work with his hand. He could do many things.

He said thank you to Jesus. Jesus had made his hand well.

Every time the man looked at his hand, he said:

"I will always use my hand to work for Jesus. I will always thank Jesus. Jesus made my hand well."

The Lord's Prayer

Our Father which art in heaven,
Hallowed be thy name.
Thy kingdom come.
Thy will be done in earth,
as it is in heaven.
Give us this day
our daily bread.

And forgive us our debts,
as we forgive our debtors.
And lead us not into temptation,
but deliver us from evil:
For thine is the kingdom,
and the power,
and the glory, for ever. Amen.

—Matthew 6:9-13.

The Golden Rule

Children, do you love each other?
Are you always kind and true?
Do you always do to others
As you'd have them do to you?

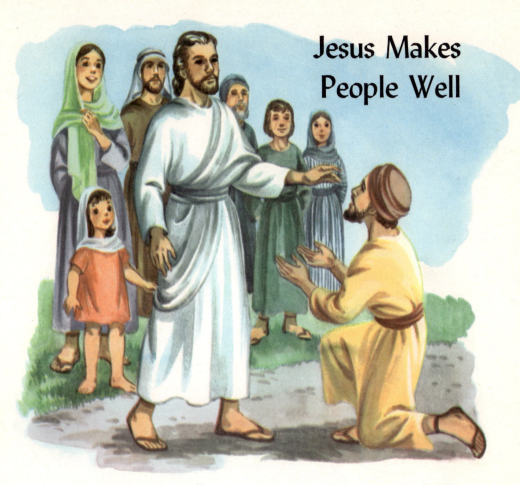

Jesus Makes People Well

A sick man was following Jesus. He said, "Lord, if you will, you can make me well."

Jesus reached out His hand and touched the man. "I will," said Jesus. "You are now well."

All the people could see that the man was strong and well.

They had been afraid to go near him because they might catch his sickness.

Now they crowded around Jesus.

Another man came to Jesus and said, "My servant is sick."

Jesus said, "I will come and make him well."

The man said, "You do not have to come. Only say the word. I know that you can make him well."

Jesus was pleased because the man believed in the things He could do.

Jesus said, "Go on your way."

The man went home. His servant was well. Jesus had not seen the servant, but He had made the servant well.

All the people were happy because Jesus made the sick people well.

Crowds of people followed Jesus.

They wanted to see what He would do. They wanted to hear what He would say.

Sometimes Jesus went to a quiet place on the mountain.

All the people would follow Him.

Jesus would tell the people about God. He wanted them to know about His home in heaven.

Jesus would tell them that He could make people well because He was God's own Son.

A Big Storm

There is a beautiful sea in the land where Jesus lived. It is called the Sea of Galilee.

When Jesus was tired, He liked to go out on the sea in a little boat.

One day Jesus had been very busy. He had made many sick people well. He needed to rest.

Jesus got into a little boat.

Jesus was too tired to work any more. "Let us go across the sea," He said.

Some of the friends of Jesus had been fishermen. They liked to go out in the boat with Jesus.

They knew that Jesus needed to rest.

They helped Him find a place to sit in the end of the boat. They were happy to see that He went to sleep.

The boat started across the Sea of Galilee. Some dark clouds blew across the sky.

The wind was blowing harder. Big waves were blowing across the sea.

But Jesus' fishermen friends were not afraid. They knew about boats.

Now the wind was blowing harder.

The waves were getting higher. It was going to be a big storm.

The waves got higher and higher. They came over the side of the boat.

The little boat was not made for such a bad storm.

Now the fishermen were afraid.

But Jesus was still asleep.

How could He sleep in such a storm?

The fishermen had no hope. They did not think their boat could get to the other side of the sea.

"We must tell Jesus," they said. "We must tell Him about the storm. He can help us."

"Teacher," they called to Him. "Teacher, don't you care if we are all killed by the storm?"

Jesus got up. He saw that His friends were afraid. He wanted to help them so they would not be hurt.

Jesus stood up in the boat. He talked to the sea and the wind. He said, "Peace, be still."

This is all He said: "Peace, be still."

The wind stopped blowing.

The waves went away.

The water was quiet again.

No one needed to be afraid of the storm any longer.

No one had ever seen anything like this happen before.

Jesus' friends were surprised!

"What kind of man is this," they said, "that even the winds and the sea do what He says!"

Jesus' friends began to see that Jesus could do anything in the world.

He could make the sick people well.

He could make people see.

He could make people hear.

He could make people walk.

He could talk to the storm and say, "Peace, be still."

He could make even the wind and the waves listen to Him.

A Little Lunch Basket

A boy and his mother lived near the beautiful Sea of Galilee.

The boy heard about Jesus.

He wanted to see the man who could make sick people well. He wanted to hear the things that Jesus would teach.

One day the boy said to his mother, "Mother, will you let me go to hear the great Teacher today?"

His mother said, "Yes, you may go. I will give you a little lunch."

The mother took five small barley cakes and two fish. She put them in a little basket.

Maybe you never had barley cakes and fish for lunch. This is what the boy had all the time.

The boy took his little basket of lunch. He started walking toward the Sea of Galilee.

Many people went to see Jesus near the Sea of Galilee. The boy hoped he would see Jesus today.

He found a crowd of people. He knew these people had come to see Jesus. Yes— there He was!

The boy saw a mother with a child who could not walk. The mother brought the child to Jesus. And then the child walked.

The boy saw many sick people. They were trying to get near Jesus.

Jesus felt sorry for the people. He knew how much they wanted His help.

Jesus began to make the sick people well. He helped all those who came to Him.

Jesus had been busy all day. It was getting late.

"The people are hungry," His helpers said. "Shall we send them away to get something to eat?"

Jesus said, "You give them something to eat."

His helpers looked all around. "We do not have any food," they said. "There is no place to get food around here."

Jesus said, "Does anyone have food?"

The helpers went around and asked all the people.

Andrew said, "There is a boy here. He has a lunch of five barley cakes and two fish."

"Bring them to me," Jesus said.

Andrew said to the boy, "Will you give your lunch to Jesus?" The boy was happy to give his lunch to Jesus.

Then Jesus told His helpers what to do. The people were to sit down on the grass.

The people were to sit so that 50 would be together or 100 would be together.

The helpers did what Jesus said. They did not know how He could feed so many people.

Jesus took the barley cakes and the two fish. All the people were watching. He looked up to heaven.

He said thank you to God for all His good gifts.

Jesus wanted all the people to know that it was God who did these wonderful things.

He wanted them to learn that He was God's own Son.

After He thanked God for the barley cakes, He began to break them into little pieces.

He gave the pieces to His helpers.

The helpers began passing the barley cakes to all the hungry people.

They began passing the fish to all the hungry people.

There were more and more cakes. There were more and more fish.

Every one had something to eat. They passed the food again.

More than 5,000 people were sitting on the grass. Every one had enough to eat. No one was hungry.

There was still food in the baskets.

Jesus said, "Pick up all the pieces. Do not leave any of the food."

His helpers picked up twelve baskets full of food.

How happy the boy was. Jesus had done a wonderful thing. Jesus had made enough food for all the people.

Jesus loved the people. He wanted to show them how wonderful God is.

And the boy helped by giving his lunch to Jesus. He was happy to be a helper for Jesus.

Jesus and a Blind Man

"Please help me. I can not see! Please help me. I can not see!"

A blind man was calling for help.

He could not see to cross the street.

He could not find his way home.

He could not work, for no one had any work that a blind man could do.

He had to stand on the street and beg for help.

This man had always been blind.

He was blind when he was a baby.

He was blind when he was a boy.

He grew up to be a man, but he was still blind.

He had never seen his mother.

He had never seen the sunshine or the flowers.

No one could make his eyes better.

One day Jesus was in the city. He saw the blind man.

Some of Jesus' helpers were with Him. They were talking to Jesus about the blind man.

Jesus wanted His helpers to know how great God is. He wanted them to know that He was doing God's work.

Jesus walked over to the blind man. He got down on the ground. He made some mud from the dust on the ground.

Jesus put the mud on the eyes of the blind man.

He said to the man, "Go wash in the pool of Siloam."

The blind man went to the pool. He washed his eyes.

What a wonderful thing! He could see!

He could see the sunshine. He could see the flowers. He could see the people who always helped him.

He was very happy. He ran home. Now he could see his mother's face.

How happy he was to get home.

His mother and father were happy.

Many people came to see the man. They knew he had always been blind.

"Can he really see?" they asked. "Maybe it is a different man."

But it was the very same man. His mother and his father knew him.

He told them how Jesus put mud on his eyes and told him to wash in the pool of Siloam. He told them how wonderful it was to see.

"Jesus is the Son of God," the man said. "He can do wonderful things. I will always give thanks to Him."

A Man on a Trip

Robbers were hiding behind a rock.

They were waiting for a man on a trip.

One robber said, "When a man comes along, jump on him. Take his money. Then run away fast."

"Take everything you can," another one said.

Then they saw a man come down the road. He was on a trip to another city.

He had a hard trip. The road was full of rocks.

There was a large rock ahead. All at once the robbers jumped out.

They hit the man and beat him. They took his money. They took his coat.

They took everything. Then they ran away.

The poor man could not go on his trip. He could not get up off the road.

Would some one come along to help him? This was a hard, rocky road. He did not know if help would come.

Then there were footsteps.

Some one was coming!

A man came along the road. He worked in God's house. He should do kind things.

He looked at the man who was hurt.

Then he turned away. He walked on. He did not stop to help.

The poor man was still on the road.

He heard more footsteps.

Another man was coming!

This man worked in God's house, too.
He should help a man who was hurt.

He looked at the hurt man.

Then he turned away. He walked on.
He did not try to help.

What would happen to the hurt man?
Would he be left to die by the side of the
road?

No—another man was coming.

The hurt man heard, "Clip-clop, clip-
clop. Clip-clop, clip-clop." This man was
riding a little donkey.

The man was a Samaritan. His people were not friends with the people of the hurt man.

"But this man needs my help," the Samaritan man said. "I must see what I can do for him."

The Samaritan man went to the hurt man. He washed the hurt places. He put soft cloth on them. The hurt man felt better.

"I will help you get on my donkey," he told the hurt man.

He took the man to an inn.

"Please take good care of this man," he told the innkeeper.

"I will give you some money to take care of him. If you need more, I will pay you when I come back."

The Samaritan went on his way. The hurt man got well.

Jesus told this story. Then He said, "Which man was a good friend to the hurt man?"

Every one said, "The Samaritan was a good friend."

Jesus wanted every one to learn to help other people.

A Man Says Thank You

Ten men were standing far away. They were calling and calling.

They saw Jesus coming. They wanted Him to hear them.

Why did the ten men stand so far away? Why would no one talk to them?

The ten men were very sick. No one wanted to catch their sickness.

They had to stay far away. They had to hold up their hands and call, "We are not clean! We are not clean!"

The ten men lived far away from the town. They could not see their families. They could not talk to their friends.

No one could help them. No one could make them well.

The ten men had heard about Jesus. Jesus had made many people well.

66

"He made blind men able to see," one man said.

"He made people's legs strong and well so they could walk again," another man said.

"Maybe Jesus will help us. We must call to Him if we see Him."

The ten sick men watched the road.

Then one day they saw Jesus coming. "There is Jesus!" they said.

They walked as close as they could. They called, "Jesus, Master, help us."

Jesus heard them calling. He wanted to help them.

Jesus went near and talked to them. "Go to see the men who help in God's house," Jesus told them.

The sick men began walking away. A wonderful thing happened. The sickness went away.

They looked at their hands, their arms, their faces. They were not sick any longer. They were well!

One man turned back to say thank you to Jesus. He threw himself down at Jesus' feet.

Jesus was glad that one man said, "Thank you, Jesus."

He looked around. He had made ten men well. Where were the others?

The others were walking home. They were happy to be well. But they were not thinking about Jesus.

Jesus was sorry that the others did not come back to say thank you. He said, "Were there not ten? Where are the nine?"

The other nine were very happy. But they did not even come back to say thank you to Jesus.

Jesus said to the one man, "Get up, and go home. Because you believed I could help you, you are well."

The man ran to tell his family and friends. He would always remember to say thank you to Jesus. Jesus had made him well.

Jesus and the Children

"Come on. Let us run," said some of the children.

"Maybe we shall be the first to see Jesus," said another one.

"Now wait for us," the mothers called. "Do not run too far away."

The children were happy. They wanted to see Jesus.

They knew that Jesus was talking to the people not far away.

Soon they saw many, many people.

"Jesus must be here," they said.

"Yes," the mothers said. "We can see Him through the crowd of people."

As the children walked toward Jesus, His helpers saw them.

"Take the children away," they said. "Jesus is very busy. He has much work to do."

But Jesus saw the children.

Jesus said, "Let the little children come unto me."

Jesus loved the children. He took them in His arms.

He put His hands on their heads. He talked to them.

The children were happy. As they walked home, they sang this song:

Jesus said, "Come unto me."

Jesus said, "Come unto me."

A Man in a Tree

Zacchaeus stood up as tall as he could.
"It is no use," he said. "I can not see
the road. I shall not see Jesus when He
walks along the road."

Zacchaeus walked along behind the
crowd of people. He was a little man.

All the people were taller than he was. He could not see.

He ran ahead. He came to a tree. He knew what to do.

"I can climb this tree," he said.

Carefully he stepped from branch to branch.

"This is fine," he said as he sat on a branch of the tree. "I did want to see Jesus very much."

Soon Jesus and His helpers came along the road.

Jesus was talking to people and helping people.

Just as Jesus came to the tree, He stopped. He looked up.

Then Zacchaeus had a happy surprise. Jesus called him by name.

"Zacchaeus, come down," Jesus said. "Today I must stay at your house."

Zacchaeus came down. He ran to Jesus. He would be happy to take Jesus to his home.

Some of the people did not like this. "Zacchaeus is a bad man," they said to each other.

"His friends are bad, too. Jesus should not eat with them."

But Jesus wanted to help Zacchaeus. He knew that Zacchaeus could be a good man.

Jesus wanted to teach Zacchaeus how to be good.

While they were eating, Jesus talked to Zacchaeus.

Zacchaeus knew that he had not been good. Sometimes he had taken too much money from people.

He knew that was wrong.

Now he was sorry.

Zacchaeus said to Jesus, "Lord, I am going to give half of my money to the poor people. If I have taken too much money from any one, I will give back four times as much."

Zacchaeus was happy. The great Teacher had come to his home today.

He would always try to do the things Jesus wanted him to do.

Jesus' Good Friends

Jesus had some good friends. They were named Mary and Martha, and their brother was Lazarus. All of them loved Jesus.

Whenever Jesus came, Martha would work hard to have a nice dinner. Mary would sit and listen to Jesus.

One time Martha said, "Jesus, tell my sister to help me."

Jesus said, "Martha, Martha, you give me good dinners. But it is better to listen to me."

One time when Jesus was far away, Lazarus got very sick. No one could make him well. He died.

Mary and Martha were very sad. They sent for Jesus.

Jesus was sad, too. He loved His friends very much.

Jesus went to the tomb. He called, "Lazarus, come out."

Right away, Lazarus walked out of the tomb, living again! People saw him walk. They heard him talk.

They knew that Jesus was God's Son. They saw that He could make people live again.

Mary and Martha said thank you over and over to Jesus.

Mary had a wonderful gift for Jesus. She had some sweet perfume.

She put it on Jesus' head and His feet.

Jesus' helpers said, "Mary should not use all that wonderful perfume. She had to pay too much money for it."

Jesus said, "Mary has done something nice for me. Whenever people tell about me, they will tell about Mary's wonderful gift."

Jesus Says Good-by

Jesus always told people about God, His Father in heaven. He told them about heaven.

Jesus told people how to live good lives. Then they could go to live in heaven some day.

Jesus knew that He would be going there soon. His work on earth was almost done.

Jesus knew that His friends could not go with Him now.

He wanted them to know how beautiful it is in heaven. He wanted them to know that some day they could live there with Him.

Jesus' friends were sad when He said He was going away. His helpers did not know what they would do.

Jesus told them not to be sorry. Here is what Jesus said. These are His own words:

Let not your heart be troubled:
Ye believe in God, believe also in me.
In my Father's house are many mansions:
if it were not so,
I would have told you.
I go to prepare a place for you.
And if I go and prepare a place for you,
I will come again,
and receive you unto myself;
that where I am,
there ye may be also.

—*John 14:1-3.*

Jesus had been very kind and good.
He had helped many people.
He had made many sick people well.
But there were some bad men who did not like Jesus. They were always trying to hurt Him.

Jesus knew that He must die. But He would live again. Then He would go to live in heaven.

That is why He said good-by. He was going home to heaven.

Jesus
Goes Home

Jesus' work on earth was done.

There were bad men who did not like Jesus. They put Him on a cross. Jesus died.

His friends cried. They were so very sad.

One day they walked to the tomb. They saw an angel.

The angel said, "Jesus is not here. He is living. Come, see the place where He was."

Jesus' friends could see that He was not there. How happy they were.

Jesus was walking and talking with people. He was not dead. He was living again.

One day Jesus took some of His friends
to a beautiful hill.

He told them that He was going home.
His home was in heaven. It was with God,
His Father in heaven.

Then Jesus held up His hands. He went
right up into heaven.

Jesus' friends saw Him go away. They knew He was in heaven with God.

They told people how Jesus had died and then lived again.

A friend named Mary said, "I saw Him in the garden. He talked to me. He made me happy again."

A man said, "One day we were walking along the road. All at once, Jesus was with us. He talked to us as we walked along. Then He went away."

Jesus' helpers said, "One night we were all together. All at once, Jesus came. He showed us that He was living."

Jesus' friends knew that they could talk with Jesus. He was living in heaven. When they prayed, they talked to Him.

Today, when we pray, Jesus hears us. He is in heaven with God, but He hears us when we talk to Him.

Praise God

Praise God, from whom all blessings
    flow;
Praise Him, all creatures here below;
Praise Him above, ye heav'nly host;
Praise Father, Son, and Holy Ghost.

Father, We Thank Thee

Father, we thank Thee for the night,
And for the pleasant morning light,
For rest and food and loving care,
And all that makes the day so fair.

Help us to do the things we should,
To be to others kind and good,
In all we do, in work or play,
To grow more loving ev'ry day.

—*Rebecca Weston*

The New Coat

One day a little boy's mother went to the store and bought him a coat.

The boy was pleased. When he tried it on, it was just right.

He said, "Oh, thank you, Mother. Thank you for my nice new coat."

The mother said, "Don't thank me; thank the storekeeper."

The little boy went to the store. He said, "I came to thank you for my nice new coat."

The storekeeper said, "Don't thank me; thank the man who made the coat for you."

The little boy ran to the man. He said, "Thank you; thank you for my nice new coat."

The man said, "Don't thank me; I only made the coat. Thank the man who made the cloth."

The boy went to the mills.

He saw all the people making cloth.

He saw one man who was standing near.

He went to the man and said, "Oh, thank you; thank you for my nice new coat."

The man said, "Don't thank me; thank the farmer who brought the wool."

The little boy ran to the farmer.

He said, "Oh, thank you, farmer; thank you for my nice new coat."

The farmer said, "Don't thank me; my sheep gave the wool to me. Go to the pasture and thank my sheep."

The boy went to the pasture where the sheep were eating the grass.

He walked to a kind old mother sheep and said, "Thank you, sheep; thank you for my nice new coat. It feels so good and warm."

The sheep said, "Oh, don't thank me; I only gave my wool. Thank God who made my wool grow."

The boy looked up to heaven.

He said, "Thank you, God. Thank you for my nice new coat."

God Made the World

Look all around!
Look up and down!
What do you see?
You see the world that God made.
Once there was no world.
There was only God in heaven.

God made the earth. He made the land
and the water. It was very dark.

God said, "Let there be light." And there
was light.

God called the light day. He called the
darkness night.

God made the sun to give us light and keep us warm. He made the moon to shine at night.

God made the heavens and all the stars that shine.

God put the water into seas. He made fish to live in the seas.

On the dry land God made grass. He made seeds to grow flowers and food. He made all the trees.

God saw that it was good.

God made birds. He gave them wings to fly through the heavens. He gave them pretty feathers.

God made all the animals. He made some animals to climb trees. He made some animals to run fast.

Look all around you. See the beautiful world God made!

God saw that it was good.

God made a man to live in this beautiful world. He made the man so he could talk. He made the man so he could think.

The man's name was Adam. He was the first man to live in the world.

Adam gave names to all the birds and animals.

God made a woman to be a helper to the man. The woman's name was Eve.

Adam and Eve lived in a beautiful garden. They saw all the wonderful things God made.

Adam and Eve took care of the garden and kept it beautiful.

The Great Ladder

"How tired I am," Jacob said.

"I have been walking all day. The sun is almost gone. Soon it will be dark. I must find a place to stop."

Jacob walked slowly. He was sorry to go away from his kind mother. He would miss his father. His father was old and blind.

But he was not sorry to go away from his brother. He had done something wrong to his brother. That is why he had to go away.

Here was a place to stop. It was just an open place with some stones. But he was very tired.

Jacob lay down. He put his head on a stone.

Now it was very dark. The stars were shining in the sky.

Jacob looked at the beautiful stars that God made. Soon he was asleep.

While he was sleeping, Jacob had a dream. He saw a big ladder. It reached from earth to heaven.

He saw many angels. Some angels were going up the ladder. Some angels were going down the ladder.

Jacob dreamed that God was at the top of the long ladder. This is what God said to him:

"I am the God of your father. I will give you the land where you are sleeping. I will give you the land in all directions, for you will have many children and a large family.

"I am with you. I will keep you safe in the places where you are going.

"I will bring you back to this land. I will never leave you. I will keep my word to you."

When Jacob got up, he said, "God must be in this place. This is the house of God. It is the gate of heaven."

Jacob took the stone where he had put his head.

"I will mark the place with this stone," he said. "I will call this place 'The House of God.'"

Jacob went on his way. He was away for many years.

When his brother was not angry, Jacob came home again.

God kept His word to Jacob. God took care of him. God gave him the land for his own family.

God
Sends
Food

"Mother, give me a drink of water," said one little boy.

His mother said, "There is no water."

The little boy was crying. "I am so hot. I want a drink of water."

The mother looked around. Many children were crying for water.

The people were going a long way. God was going to give them a new land.

God told them that He would take care of them on the way. But it was a long way. They were sad.

The people talked to Moses. The people told him how sad they were.

"We must have some water," they said. "Listen to the children cry. We have had no water for three days."

Moses prayed to God.

They came to a place where there was water. But it was not good.

God told Moses what to do. "Take that tree. Throw it into the water."

"Oh, it is good," the people said. "Now the water is sweet."

"God gave us water to drink," Moses told the people.

Another time there was no water.

God said to Moses, "Talk to the rock and it will give you water."

Moses held up his stick. He hit the rock! The water came out! How good it was to drink!

Every one had food to eat, too. God sent food every day. It was called manna.

Every morning the people found manna on the ground. It was white. It was very good to eat.

Each one picked up enough manna for himself.

Each mother picked up her manna.

Each father picked up his manna.

Each child picked up his manna.

The children loved manna.

One day each week, God would send much more manna. Every one would pick up enough for two days.

The people always had enough manna to eat.

They said thank you to God for giving them food and water.

The Fall of Jericho

God had said He would give His people a new land to live in.

Now they had come to this new land.

But the people there were big. They had kings and soldiers.

Every city had big walls. How could they get in?

"Do not be afraid," God told the people. "I will take care of you. I will give you the land."

God told Joshua to take the people to the new land.

"I will give you the city of Jericho," God said.

The people knew that God would take care of them. He had given them water. He had given them food. Now He would give them the land.

God told Joshua what he should do.

Every day they must march around the walls of the city of Jericho.

First their own soldiers would march.

Then seven men with horns would march.

Then all the people would march. No one was to talk or shout. They must be very quiet.

This is what they would do every day for six days.

On the seventh day they would march around the city seven times. The seven men would blow the horns.

Then the people would shout with a great shout. And the walls of the city would fall down flat.

The people wondered how God would do this. But God always did what He said He would do.

The people got everything ready.

The first day they marched around the walls of Jericho. The soldiers marched first. The seven men with horns marched next. All the people marched.

The next day every one marched again. They marched every day for six days.

On the seventh day, they marched around the city seven times. The seven men blew the horns.

The people shouted with a great shout. The walls of Jericho fell down flat.

God's people went in and took the city God had given them.

DAVID HELPS
THE KING

David looked all around.

He did not see a bear. He did not see a lion. His sheep were safe.

He looked at all the little lambs. Each one was near its mother.

David was a shepherd boy.

In the morning he would take the sheep to the field of green grass. He would find water for them to drink.

He would watch for animals that might hurt the sheep.

Sometimes David would play his harp. He would sing this song:

> The Lord is my shepherd;
> I shall not want.

David knew that God took care of him. God would keep him safe.

Sometimes other people would hear David sing. "What a pretty song," they would say.

One day the king of all the land was very sick.

One man said, "I know some one who will make the king feel better. David the shepherd boy can play the harp and sing beautiful songs. David will make the king feel better."

The man from the king's house went to find David. He said, "Come and play for the king. He is sick. You will make him feel better."

David went to the king's house. He played the harp. He sang beautiful songs. Perhaps he sang, "The Lord is my shepherd."

The king felt better. He was not sick any more.

"David is a good helper," said the king. "I want him to come and play for me all the time."

David said, "I will come back to play for you again. But I want to go back and take care of my sheep. I like to be a shepherd boy."

David
and the
Giant

David liked to be a shepherd boy.

Sometimes he would think about his brave brothers. They were soldiers of the king.

One day David's father said, "I want you to go to see your brothers. I want to send them some food."

David got ready for the trip. He took the food. He went a long way. He found his brothers.

"Why do you stay here so long?" David said.

His brothers said, "Those soldiers over there want to take the land away from our king. The soldiers are big. One soldier is like a giant. You can see him tomorrow if you wait."

David wanted to see the giant. His name was Goliath.

The next day Goliath came out. He walked up and down.

He called: "Why are you afraid? Will no one fight with me? Send some one to fight with me!"

He laughed at the soldiers.

Would some of David's big brothers fight the giant? No! They were afraid.

David said, "I would not be afraid to fight the giant."

Some of the soldiers heard him. Fight the giant? A shepherd boy? This was a surprise!

One of them told the king that David would fight the giant.

The king was surprised. "You are just a boy," the king said. "I can not let you go to fight the giant."

David said to the king: "One time I was watching my sheep. A lion came and got a lamb. I ran after the lion and killed it.

"Another time a bear came after a lamb. I killed the bear, too.

"God took care of me when the lion and the bear came. God will take care of me when I fight the giant."

David did not have anything to use to fight. He had only his slingshot.

He picked up five small stones and put them into his bag. He took his little slingshot.

Goliath saw him coming. He began to laugh and call to David.

"What are you going to fight with?"

"I do not need anything," said David. "God is helping me."

David took one of the small stones. He put it in his slingshot. He began to swing it around and around. Then he let go.

There went the stone!

It hit the head of the giant. Goliath fell
down dead.

The soldiers with Goliath ran away.
Now they were afraid.

David was happy. God had taken care
of him. He sang a beautiful song. He said,
"The Lord is my shepherd."

Bread for Elijah

Elijah was a good man. He worked hard for God.

One day he was very tired and hungry. He saw a woman picking up sticks.

"Will you give me a drink of water?" Elijah said.

The woman went to get the water.

Elijah called, "Will you bring me some bread, too?"

The woman said, "I have only a little meal and a little oil. I am going to make some bread.

"I was picking up sticks to start the fire. I am going to give some bread to my little boy. I am going to eat some bread. After this is gone, we will die."

Elijah said, "Do not be afraid. Make some bread for me to eat.

"Then make some bread for you and your son.

"God wants me to tell you this: 'You shall always have meal and oil.'"

Every day the woman made some bread for Elijah.

Every day she made some bread for her little boy.

There was always meal and oil in the jar to make more bread.

Elijah was happy to have food to eat. The woman was good to him. She made bread for him every day.

One day the woman was crying.

Elijah said, "What is the matter?"

"My little boy was very sick," she said. "He has died. Oh, how I loved my little boy."

Elijah wanted to help the woman. She had been kind to him. Now he wanted to do something for her.

"Give me your boy," he said. He picked up the boy and carried him up the stairway to his room.

Elijah prayed to God.

Elijah said, "Oh, God, let the little boy live again."

God heard his prayer. And God made the little boy live again.

Elijah took the boy to his mother.

"See, here is your son," he said. "God has made him live again."

The mother was happy. She thanked Elijah. She said thank you to God.

"Now I know you are a man of God," she said. "God has given me my little boy again."

New Basic Bible Vocabulary

Standard's Basic Bible Reader, Grade Two: *I Read About God's Gifts* follows the Basic Bible Reader, Grade One: *I Read About God's Love*. First in the series of five readers is the Basic Bible Primer: *I Learn to Read About Jesus*.

I Read About God's Gifts contains a total of 698 different words. Of this number, 592 are words used in public school pre-primers, primers, first and second readers; 48 are the Bible words repeated from *I Learn to Read About Jesus* and *I Read About God's Love;* and 58 are introduced as new Bible words, that is, words in Scripture quotations and words necessary to the Bible stories. The words in poetry are exempt from the vocabulary control.

The 58 words in the list to follow are the Bible words first used in this book and are a part of Standard's Basic Bible Vocabulary.

Page		Page	
8	. . .	22	net
9	. . .	23	James
10	Herod's		John
11	. . .	24	. . .
12	. . .	25	. . .
13	. . .	26	. . .
14	. . .	27	. . .
15	Saviour	28	. . .
	Christ	29	. . .
16	. . .	30	Bethesda
17	glory	31	. . .
	peace	32	. . .
	starry	33	. . .
18	Nazareth	34	. . .
	carpenter	35	. . .
	Joseph's	36	. . .
19	. . .	37	. . .
20	. . .	38	Lord's
21	Peter		art
	Andrew		hallowed

	daily	63	. . .
39	forgive	64	Samaritan
	debts	65	. . .
	debtors	66	. . .
	lead	67	. . .
	temptation	68	. . .
	deliver	69	. . .
	evil	70	. . .
	power	71	. . .
	Amen	72	. . .
40	. . .	73	. . .
41	. . .	74	Zacchaeus
42	sickness	75	. . .
	servant	76	. . .
43	. . .	77	. . .
44	Galilee	78	Martha
45	. . .		Lazarus
46	. . .		died
47	. . .	79	tomb
48	. . .	80	Mary's
49	. . .	81	. . .
50	. . .	82	troubled
51	barley		ye
52	. . .		also
53	. . .		mansions
54	. . .		prepare
55	. . .		receive
56	. . .	83	. . .
57	blind	84	. . .
58	. . .	85	. . .
59	Siloam	86	. . .
60	. . .	87	. . .
61	. . .	88	. . .
62	. . .	89	. . .

90	. . .	107	. . .
91	. . .	108	Jericho
92	wool		Joshua
93	. . .	109	. . .
94	. . .	110	. . .
95	. . .	111	. . .
96	. . .	112	. . .
97	. . .	113	. . .
98	Adam	114	. . .
99	Eve	115	David's
100	. . .	116	Goliath
101	. . .		fight
102	. . .	117	slingshot
103	. . .	118	. . .
104	. . .	119	. . .
105	. . .	120	Elijah
106	manna		

Cumulative Basic Bible Vocabulary

Through Grade Two

The following list includes all of the words introduced as new Bible words in the Basic Bible Primer, Grade One Reader, and Grade Two Reader.

Adam	David's	Goliath
also	dead	hallowed
Amen	debts	Hannah
Andrew	debtors	Hannah's
angel	deliver	harp
Anna	den	harvest
ark	departed	heat
art	destroy	heaven
baa	die	Herod
barley	died	Herod's
behold	dove	highest
Bethesda	east	hosanna
Bethlehem	Eli	inn
between	Eli's	innkeeper
Bible	Elijah	Jacob
blind	Eve	James
born	evil	Jericho
bow	fight	Jerusalem
camel	flesh	Jesus
camels'	flood	Jesus'
carpenter	forbid	Jews
cease	forgive	John
child	frankincense	Joseph
Christ	Galilee	Joseph's
covenant	Genesis	Joshua
daily	gift	Judaea
Daniel	glory	king
Daniel's	God	kingdom
David	God's	king's

law
Lazarus
lead
leadeth
lie
lo
Lord
Lord's
maketh
manger
manna
mansions
Martha
Mary
Mary's
Matthew
Miriam
Moses
myrrh
Nazareth
net
Noah
pasture
peace
perfume

Peter
power
pray
prayed
prayer
praying
prepare
presented
princess
Psalm
receive
remaineth
ruler
Samaritan
Samuel
Saviour
seedtime
servant
sheep
shepherd
shone
sick
sickness
Siloam
Simeon

slingshot
Son
stable
star
starry
such
suffer
teacher
temple
temptation
token
tomb
treasures
troubled
unto
wise
Wise-man
Wise-men
wool
worship
worshipped
ye
young
Zacchaeus